In a Mess

Written by
Stephen Rickard

Ransom

The dog is a mess.

The dog is a bit dim.
It is in a lot of mud.

The cat is not a mess.

The cat is not dim.
It is not in a lot of mud.

The big fat rat is not a mess.

The big fat rat is not dim.
It did not get into the mud.

Is the duck a mess?

No. The duck is not a mess.

Is the hen a mess?

No. The hen is not a mess.

The hen has no mud on it.

Is the pup a mess?

The pup is a bit
of a mess.

But the pup is not
sad!

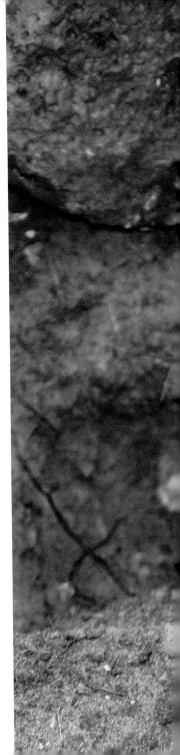

Is the rabbit a mess?

No. The rabbit is not a mess.

Is the bug a mess?

No. The bug is not a mess.

But the bug is **in** a mess!